my first
Search & Find
BOOK

ARCTURUS

ARCTURUS

This edition published in 2019 by Arcturus Publishing Limited
26/27 Bickels Yard, 151–153 Bermondsey Street,
London SE1 3HA

Illustrator: Kasia Dudziuk
Designer: Sarah Fountain
Cover designer: Ms Mousepenny
Editor: Sebastian Rydberg

ISBN: 978-1-78950-319-7
CH007020NT
Supplier 33, Date 0519 Print run 8589

Printed in China

Which two birds look exactly alike?

Find three birds with black beaks!

Which bird has caught a fish in its talons?

3

Where's the baby turtle hiding?

How many clownfish can you see?

Spot six starfish.

4

Which starfish has an extra arm?

How many fish with black and yellow stripes are there?

Which squid is the odd one out?

Who is covered in round, black spots?

Find three frogs!

Which monkey is holding a fruit?

Which two birds look exactly alike?

Which bird has a green beak?

Spot the bird carrying an apple!

Which giraffe is the tallest?

How many antelope are running?

Can you find the sleepy lion cub?

8

Which animal is taking a bath?

How many hyenas are laughing?

Which lion is roaring?

Which two rhinos look the same?

How many meerkats can you spot?

Which giraffe is the odd one out?

Can you spot the baby hedgehog?

Which squirrel is collecting nuts

Find the red-headed woodpecker.

This owl has a yellow beak.

Which badger has fallen asleep?

Which red mushroom has the most spots?

Find the snail with a stripy shell.

Which of these nests has the most hungry chicks?

Which rabbit is munching a carrot?

How many camels can you see?

Can you spot the scorpions?

Find two lizards!

Which two vultures look exactly the same?

One of these camels has an extra hump.

A bird has made its home inside this cactus.

15

Count three narwhals coming up for air.

How many polar bear cubs are there?

Which walrus has a missing tusk?

Which two penguins are exactly the same?

How many baby chicks can you see?

Our Antarctic home.

Which penguin has caught a fish?

17

Which koala is eating a leaf?

Which kangaroo can jump the highest?

How many blue birds can you see?

18

Which one of these animals doesn't have a baby?

Which Emu has three chicks?

Which two koalas look exactly alike?

19

Which animals are bathing in the river?

Find four red and yellow flowers!

Can you find three hummingbirds?

20

Which butterfly has yellow wings?

These two butterflies look exactly alike.

One of these insects looks like a flower.

Solutions

Page 3

- Matching birds
- Birds with black beaks
- Bird with a fish

Page 4

- Baby turtle
- Clownfish
- Starfish

Page 5

- Starfish
- Black and yellow stripy fish
- Odd squid out

Page 6

- Round black spots
- Frogs
- Monkey with a fruit

Page 7

- Matching birds
- A green beak
- Carrying an apple

Page 8

- Tallest giraffe
- Antelope running
- Sleepy lion cub

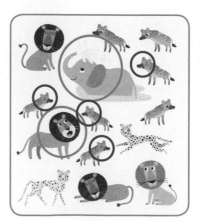

Page 9

- Taking a bath
- Roaring lion
- Laughing hyenas

Page 10
- Matching rhinos
- Meerkats
- Odd giraffe out

Page 14
- Camels
- Scorpions
- Lizards

Page 11
- Baby hedgehog
- Squirrel with nut
- Red-headed woodpecker

Page 15
- Matching vultures
- Camel with extra hump
- Bird in a cactus

Page 12
- Yellow beak owl
- Sleeping badger
- Mushroom with most spots

Page 16
- Narwhals
- Polar bear cubs
- Walrus missing a tusk

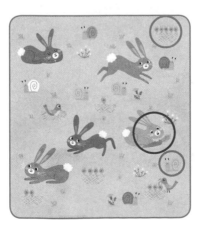

Page 13
- Stripy snail
- Nest with most chicks
- Munching rabbit

Page 17
- Matching penguins
- Baby chicks
- Penguin with a fish

Page 18

- Koala eating a leaf
- Highest kangaroo
- Blue birds

Page 20

- Animals bathing
- Orange flowers
- Hummingbirds

Page 19

- Animal with no baby
- Emu with three chicks
- Matching koalas

Page 21

- Butterfly with yellow wings
- Matching butterflies
- Insect like a flower